It's Ted Rogers!

Hello, folks, and welcome to the new 3-2-1 Dusty Bin annual. It's based on Yorkshire Television's top-rated TV quiz show compèred by yours truly.

We've lined up for you all sorts of gags, games and puzzles, and some stories, to keep you in touch with your favourite show and to give you plenty of holiday entertainment.

We can't give you any gleaming new car or dream holiday prizes, but if you get the answers wrong in this annual at least you won't go off with Dusty Bin.

So relax and enjoy yourselves. Have fun — and see you next time on the show!

"3-2-1", DUSTY BIN and THE DUSTY BIN CHARACTER are Trade Marks of Yorkshire Television Enterprises Limited.

"3-2-1" is a Yorkshire Television Production.

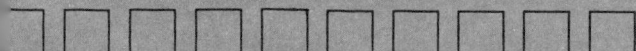

Contents

Published by IPC Magazines Ltd., King's Reach Tower, Stamford Street, London. SE1 9LS. Sole agents for Australia and New Zealand: Gordon & Gotch Ltd., South Africa: Central News Agency Ltd. Typesetting by Top Type Services Ltd., London SE6, reproduction and printing by Legotoria Editoriale Giovanni Olivotto, Vicenza, Italy.

£2.95

Ted Roger's

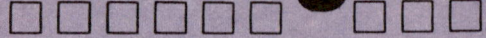

Books and Writers

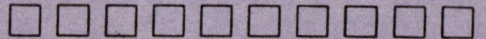

Ted Rogers — Your Quiz Master has set some questions for you on a number of subjects. Some are easy — some are not so easy. See how many you can answer correctly.

1 Who created the great detective, Sherlock Holmes?

2 In which story and play does a pirate named Smee appear?

3 From what disability did the poet Milton suffer?

4 Complete these pairs: (a) Dr. Jekyll and . . . . (b) Romeo and . . . .?

5 P.C. Wren wrote a famous book about English brothers in the French Foreign Legion. Name it.

6 Becky Sharp appears in which book by Thackeray?.

7 He wrote *The Charge of the Light Brigade*. Who did?

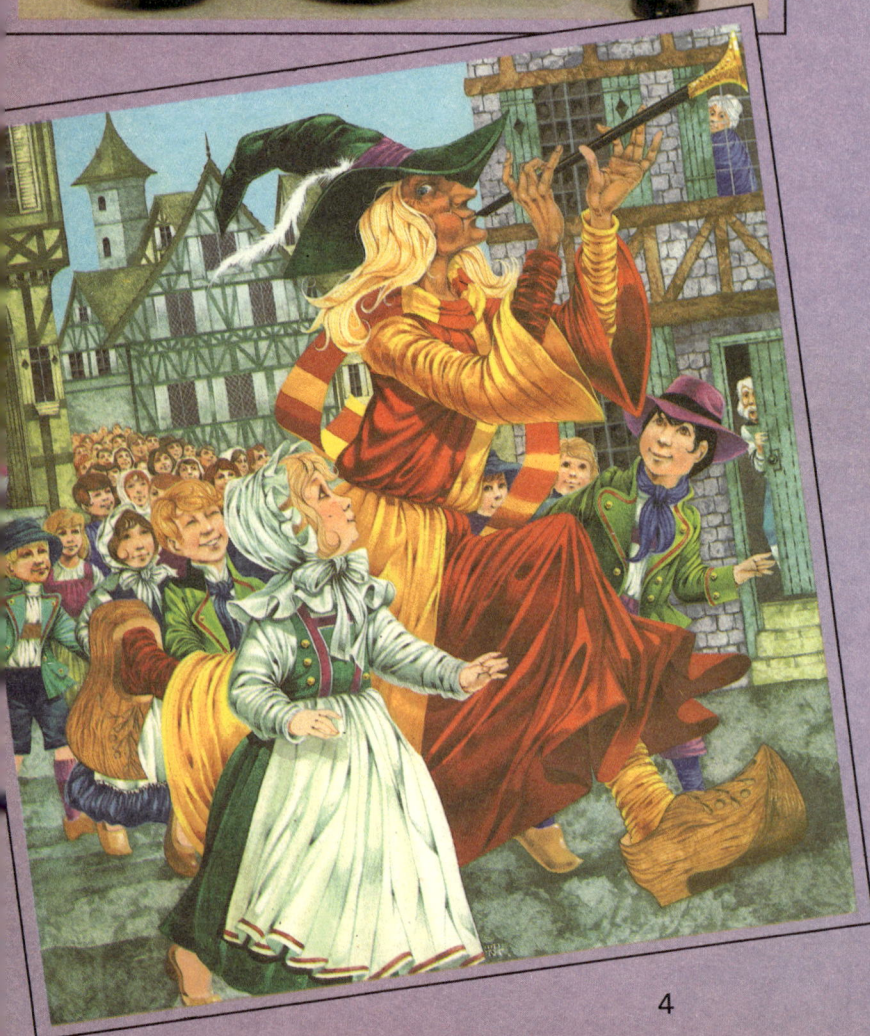

Quiz Section □□□□□□□□□□□□

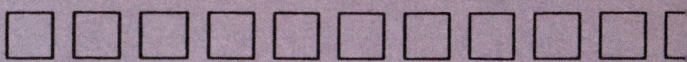

14 *My Early Life* was written by which famous Prime Minister?

15 **Who wrote *Black Beauty?***

16 Mary Shelley wrote a classic horror story, much to the delight of film-makers. Can you name it?

17 **James Bond was created by . . .?**

18 Shakespeare wrote a play with a black hero. Can you name him?

19 **Who wrote both *Animal Farm* and *1984?***

20 Can you name Welsh poet Dylan Thomas's most famous work?

8 Which book did John Bunyan start writing in Bedford Jail?

9 **Where did the Pied Piper pipe?**

10 Who, according to Shakespeare, said 'Et tu, Brute!' before dying?

11 **A famous Victorian novelist worked in a blacking factory as a boy. Who was he?**

12 *Swallows and Amazons* was written by?

13 **Which of these books is not by Dickens?** *Barnaby Rudge, Pickwick Papers, Barchester Towers?*

Continued from previous page.

21 In *Peter Pan*, who was the crocodile's most famous victim?

22 Can you name the tiger in Kipling's *Jungle Book?*

23 Name Richard Adams' famous book about rabbits.

24 Which great American river do you associate with Mark Twain's *Tom Sawyer?*

25 Who wrote about the detectives Hercule Poirot and Miss Marple?

26 Which great English poet died helping liberate Greece?

27 Name the ship in *Treasure Island.*

28 How many lines are there in a sonnet?

29 The poet Longfellow wrote about a Red Indian. Can you name him?

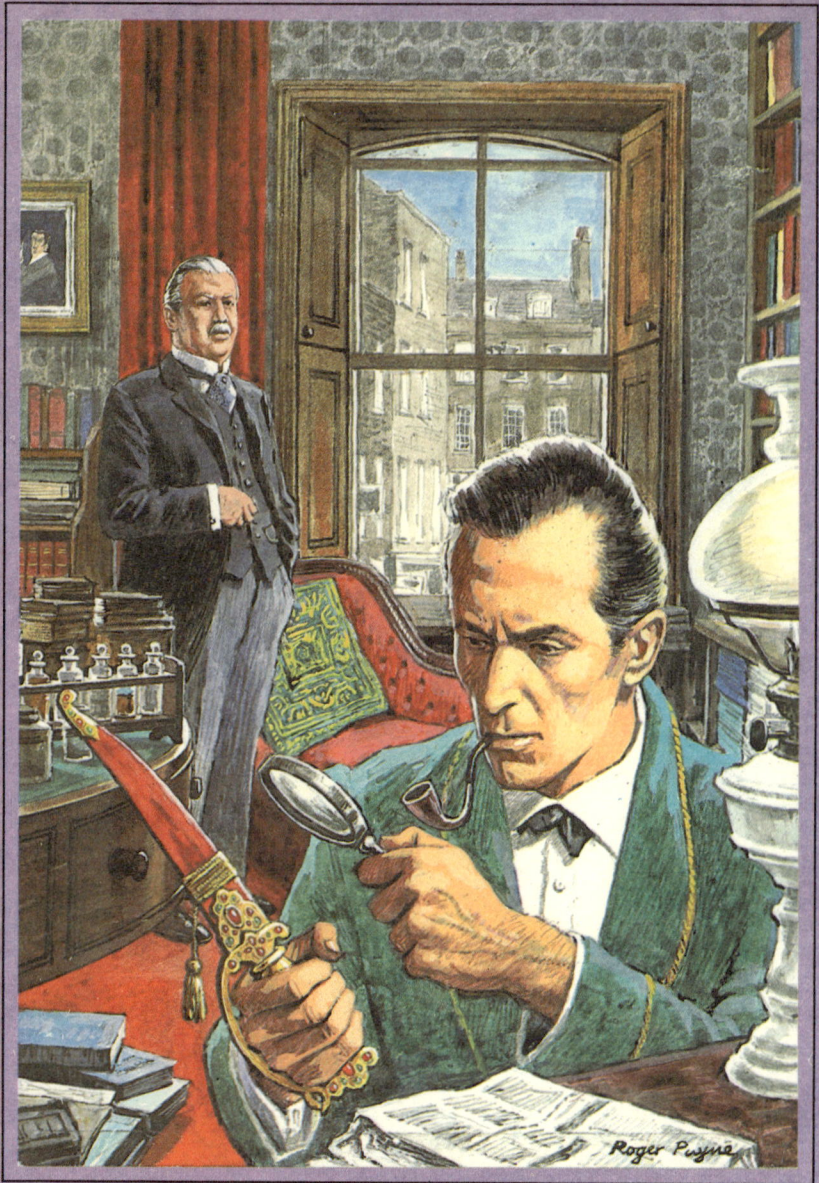

30 Who wrote about otters in *Ring of Bright Water?*

31 Name Richmal Crompton's most famous character.

32 The Brothers Grimm wrote the story of the Ugly Duckling. True or false?

33 Which of these is not by Sir Walter Scott? *Ivanhoe, Tom Jones, Rob Roy.*

34 Which area of England do you associate with the poet Wordsworth?

35 Who writest about *Paddington Bear?*

□□□□□□□□□□□**Answers**□□□□□□□□□□□

1 Sir Arthur Conan Doyle. 2 *Peter Pan.* 3 He went blind. 4 *Mr. Hyde,* by Robert Louis Stevenson: *Juliet,* by Shakespeare. 5 *Beau Geste.* 6 *Vanity Fair.* 7 Lord Tennyson. 8 *Pilgrim's Progess.* 9 Hamelin. 10 Julius Caesar. 11 Charles Dickens. 12 Arthur Ransome. 13 *Barchester Towers* is by Trollope. 14 Sir Winston Churchill. 15 Anna Sewell. 16 *Frankenstein.* 17 Ian Fleming. 18 *Othello.* 19 George Orwell. 20 *Under Milk Wood.* 21 Captain Hook. 22 Shere Khan. 23 *Watership Down.* 24 The Mississippi. 25 Agatha Christie. 26 Lord Byron, died of a fever while training troops. 27 *Hispaniola.* 28 Fourteen. 29 Hiawatha. 30 Gavin Maxwell. 31 William. 32 False. Hans Andersen wrote it. 33 *Tom Jones,* which is by Fielding. 34 The Lake District. 35 Michael Bond.

How much do YOU know?

1 Where was Napoleon born?

2 Australia's capital is Sydney. True or false?

3 Was Isambard Kingdom Brunel a great poet?

4 What, principally, did Sir Alexander Fleming discover?

5 Where was the first manned, powered flight made, and by whom?

6 Only one English king is known as 'the Great'. Who was he?

7 Where is La Scala opera house?

8 Which Scottish author has a monument in Princes Street, Edinburgh?

9 Who was President of the United States during the Civil War of 1861-65?

10 Why is Count von Zeppelin remembered?

11 Where would you expect to meet Sinhalese and Tamil people?

Continued overleaf.

Continued from previous page.

12 Who was knighted on board his flagship by Queen Elizabeth I?

13 **Why was Sir Don Bradman knighted?**

14 Where were the ancient kings of Ireland crowned?

15 **Why was Claude Grahame-White famous?**

16 Which of the film comics, Laurel and Hardy, was born in England?

17 **Who wrote** *Far from the Madding Crowd?*

This is called the Monument. It commemorates which famous event in London's history?

18 Who commanded the Allied armies on D-Day, 6th June 1944?

19 **Who was the British Empire's top air ace in World War One?**

20 Who became the first prime minister of an independent India in 1947?

21 **Which warrior nation wiped out a British Force at Isandhlwana in 1879?**

22 The Battle of the Somme was in World War Two. True or false?

23 **With what do you associate the name of Sir Frank Whittle?**

24 Which British king was killed in the New Forest by an arrow?

25 **Which great Italian scientist, who died in 1642, was arrested for his beliefs?**

26 Which is the outsider — Billy Wright, Wally Hammond, Peter May?

27 **On which Pacific island did the mutineers from HMS *Bounty* finally settle.**

28 With what type of film do you especially associate director John Ford?

Where would you expect to see this famous Tower?

Answers☐☐☐☐☐☐☐☐

Answer to Picture Question on page 8: The Great Fire of London in 1666.
Answer to Picture Question on page 9: Pisa in Italy.

1 Corsica. 2 False: Canberra. 3 No, a great engineer who built railways, bridges etc. 4 Penicillin. 5 The Wright Brothers in 1903 at Kitty-Hawk, North Carolina. 6 Alfred. 7 Milan. 8 Sir Walter Scott. 9 Abraham Lincoln. 10 For his airships. 11 In Sri Lanka, formerly Ceylon. 12 Sir Francis Drake. 13 For his amazing services to Australian cricket. 14 Tara. 15 He was the first Briton to gain an aviator's certificate — in 1909. 16 Laurel. 17 Thomas Hardy. 18 General Eisenhower. 19 The Canadian, Billy Bishop. 20 Nehru. 21 The Zulus. 22 False. In World War I — 1916. 23 The development of the jet engine. 24 William II. 25 Galileo. 26 Billy Wright was a great footballer, the others, great cricketers. 27 Pitcairn. 28 Westerns.

The Explorers

1 Which great navigator was killed in Hawaii in 1779?

2 Where did Columbus think he had got to when he sighted land in 1492?

3 Who led the first successful expedition to the South Pole?

4 Who discovered the Victoria Falls of the Zambesi River in 1855?

5 After whom is Tasmania named?

6 Who led the first successful expedition up Mount Everest in 1953?

7 Who sailed by balsa raft from Peru to Polynesia to prove that Peruvian Indians could have settled there?

8 Which huge island did John Cabot discover in 1497?

9 Which marvellous sailors rowed the seas and oceans in 'longships'?

10 Who led the first successful expedition to sail around the world, but died before the journey was over?

11 Who commanded the first British Expedition round the world?

12 Who first orbited the Earth?

13 Which famous explorer was put into an open boat on the Bay that bears his name?

1 Captain Cook. 2 The Indies (India). 3 Roald Amundsen in 1911. 4. David Livingstone. 5 The Dutch navigator Tasman. 6 Sir John Hunt. 7 Thor Heyerdahl. 8 Newfoundland. 9 The Vikings. 10 Magellan who died in 1521. 11 Sir Francis Drake. 12 A Russian cosmonaut named Yuri Gagarin in 1961. 13 Henry Hudson in 1611.

Art and Artists □ □ □ □

1 Who painted the roof of the Sistine Chapel in the Vatican?

2 Picasso was a French painter. True or false?

3 How many paintings did Van Gogh sell in his lifetime?

4 The founder of the English school of painting was born in Sudbury. He was famous for landscapes and portraits. Name him.

5 Where can the Venus de Milo be seen?

6 Which animal did the artist Stubbs frequently paint?

7 An 18th century Italian artist painted London and Venice many times. Who was he?

8 Michelangelo painted the *Mona Lisa*. True or false?

9 Which German artist painted Henry VIII and many of his courtiers?

10 A Spanish painter portrayed the horrors of war in the early 19th century. Name him.

11 The most famous sculptor of the last century was a Frenchman. Who was he?

12 Who painted a series of pictures called *The Rake's Progress?*

Music and Musicians

1 Who was the composer of *Messiah?*

2 Despite deafness, Beethoven went on composing. How many of his symphonies survive?

3 Franz Liszt was a great composer and the finest pianist of his day. What nationality was he?

4 Who wrote the opera *Aida?*

5 A great Russian composer wrote the music for the ballet *Swan Lake.* Name him.

6 Who died leaving an Unfinished Symphony?

7 Which opera did Mozart NOT compose — *Don Giovanni, The Magic Flute, Tristan and Isolde?*

8 Which great music festival is held every year in London's Royal Albert Hall?

9 Why was Stradavarius famous — and still is?

10 Music played 'largo' means that is it played fast. True or false?

All sorts of Animals

□□□□□□□□□□□□□□□□

1 Who wrote about a lioness in *Born Free?*

2 Which breed of dog is named after an English king?

3 Is a Suffolk horse Britain's heaviest?

4 A gecko is a snake — or is it?

5 What sort of noise does a death watch beetle make?

6 Wolves once roamed Britain. True or false?

7 On which animal did American Indians depend for food, shelter and clothing?

8 The springbok is the national emblem of which country?

9 Where would you find a wild cat in Britain?

10 Where do the orang-utans live?

11 Which great conqueror named a city after his beloved horse?

12 Where does a yak live?

13 Where might you find a vampire bat?

14 Dogs can see colours. True or false?

15 The horse Comanche was the only survivor of a famous battle. Name it.

Continued overleaf.

19 **What is an elver?**

20 Name the world's biggest dog.

21 **Where does the hill mynah come from?**

22 Where is the Grand National run?

23 **What is the only food that the koala bear eats?**

24 Which are the most feared jungle animals?

25 **What devilment does the Tasmanian Devil get up to?**

Continued from previous page.

16 **Which country has the Kiwi as its symbol?**

17 **Which creepy crawlie may eat its mate?**

18 Which is the largest land mammal alive today?

□□□ **Answers** □□□

1 Joy Adamson. 2 King Charles Spaniel: Charles II. 3 No, the Shire is. 4 It is a lizard. 5 Ticking. 6 True. 7 Bison, called Buffalo as a rule. 8 South Africa. 9 Scotland. 10 Borneo and Sumatra in Indonesia. 11 Alexander the Great named Bucephala in India after his horse Bucephalus. 12 Tibet. 13 Central and South America. 14 False, apparently! 15 Custer's Last Stand against Indians in 1876. 16 New Zealand. 17 Spider. 18 African elephant. 19 A young eel. 20 St. Bernard. 21 India. 22 Aintree, near Liverpool. 23 Eucalyptus leaves. 24 Driver ants. 25 It attacks sheep and poultry and is killed for that reason. Yet some Tasmanians keep them as pets!

Dusty Bin's Junior Quiz Section

DUSTY BIN'S TEASERS

1. CAN YOU IDENTIFY SIX COUNTRIES SUGGESTED IN THE PANELS BELOW?

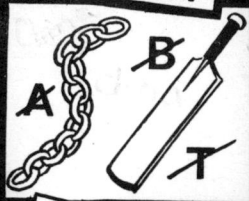

2. FOLLOW THE INSTRUCTIONS TO FIND THE WORDS WHICH DESCRIBE SOME OF THE THINGS YOU CAN FIND ON THE BEACH!

– N + 📖 – I + S =

– ES + 🍞 – L + D =

– D + 🔔 – EB =

★ – TR + 🪡 – EELE =

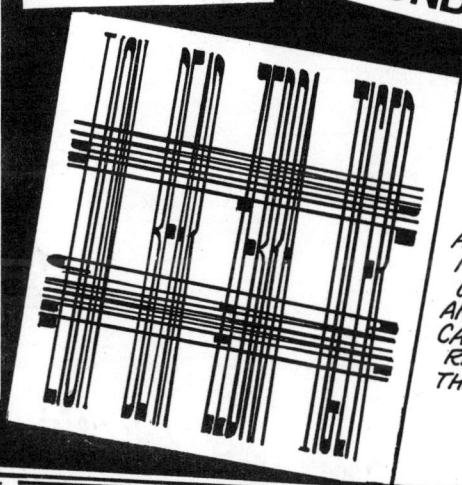

3. HERE ARE THE NAMES OF SIX ANIMALS. CAN YOU READ THEM?

4. CAN YOU IDENTIFY ALL THESE JUMBLED SHADOW SHAPES?

5. FIND THE MISSING LETTERS FROM THIS ALPHABET TO DISCOVER THE NAME OF A SPORT!

A N O J Q Z
C K T P E S
L W D V H
F X I M

ANSWERS:-
1: CANADA, POLAND, JAPAN, CHINA, SWEDEN, INDIA. 2: PEBBLES, SEAWEED, SHELLS, SAND. 3: LION, BEAR, ZEBRA, TIGER, WOLF, CAMEL (HOLD THE PAGE UP AT EYE LEVEL!) 4: ANCHOR, KNIFE, BAT, STAR, PENCIL, LADDER, SCISSORS, AXE, PAINTBRUSH, BROOM, FLAG. 5: RUGBY.

17

Dusty Bin's ANIMAL QUIZ?

HOW GOOD IS YOUR KNOWLEDGE OF THE WORLD'S WILDLIFE?

CIRCLE WHAT YOU THINK THE CORRECT ANSWER IS...

1. HOW FAST CAN A CHEETAH RUN?
   A. 10 M.P.H.
   B. 75 M.P.H.
   C. 90 M.P.H.

2. A ZEBRA CAN MAKE A BARKING NOISE.
   A. TRUE
   B. FALSE

3. A GROUP OF LIONS IS CALLED A...
   A. DEN
   B. MANE
   C. PRIDE

4. WHAT DOES A GIRAFFE FEED ON?
   A. TREE BARK
   B. LEAVES and THORNS
   C. GRASS

5. HOW MUCH DOES A RHINOCEROS WEIGH?
   A. 1 TON
   B. 2 TONS
   C. 4 TONS

6. IS THE ELEPHANT THE LARGEST LAND MAMMAL?
   A. YES
   B. NO

ANSWERS. 1. B. 2. A. 3. C. 4. B. 5. B. 6. A.

The Cottage Garden

1 What do most cottage gardens have some-where? Join the dots from 1 to 40 and you will have the answer.

2 Here are two of the gardener's friends. Write their names in the panels below. What is the main difference between them?

3 Cottage gardens seem to grow a special selection of flowers, here are some of them. How many of them do you recognise? Write their names in the panels beside them.

GET THIS BIN PARCELLED UP

BORIN

YENJN

ESU

TREEP

RIAMA

KAMR

Fit this on it
2 Which of the four jigsaw pieces will fit into the empty space below.

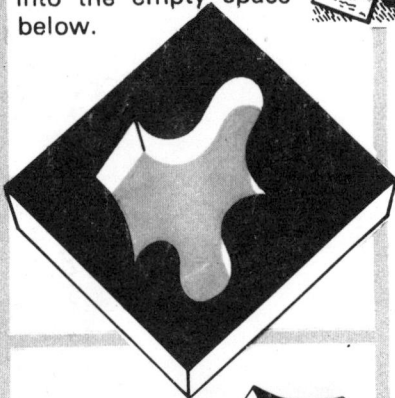

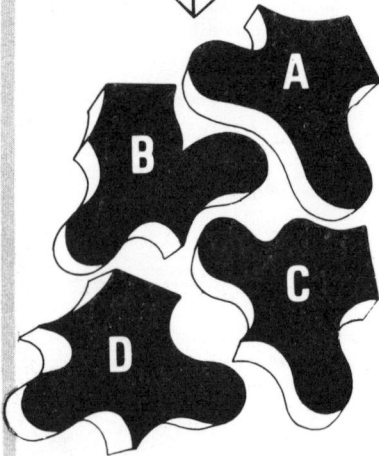

A
B
C
D

1 The typewriter broke down and typed all the letters in the wrong order. Can you unscramble them and write the correct labels on the presents so that the postman can deliver them.

An attractive problem
3 Write the names of these objects in the circle in the spaces round the outside of the circle, then write the names of those that are attracted by a magnet.

Pencil Rubber

The magnetic objects are

_____

_____

_____

Answers:
(1) The names are: 1 Jenny, 2 Robin, 3 Peter, 4 Sue, 5 Mark, 6 Maria.
(2) D. (3) Penknife, nibs, eraser (or rubber), cotton, pins, matches. The magnetic objects are: penknife, nibs, pins.

20

It's a Dog's Life

1 Here are five dogs. Can you name them and say which comes from each of the following countries? Germany–Egypt–England Russia–Afghanistan. What are these five dogs noted for? Fill in their names in the panels and what they are noted for–above.

H

A   H

B

D

F   S

2 Dogs on parade. These six dogs are walking smartly in a line. They all have black markings and these are of two patterns but there is one dog that is slightly different, which one is it?

a   b   c   d   e   f

21

In the country

1 A ramble in the country is more interesting if you can recognise the things you see. There are ten things for you to name in this picture. To help you the first letter of each word is given.

2 Shade in the shapes marked with a cross with green pencil and those with a dot with black and you will find a little animal that spends its time burrowing. What is it?

Answers:

(1) Clouds, Horse Chestnut, Oak, Poplar, Heron, Moorhen, stream otter, stile, hedge. (2) A mole. (3) A has no black spot in the centre of the top flower. (4) A windmill. Only you know whether you have seen one and where. (5) A badger's home is called a set.

3 Here are four pots of flowers, that all seem the same. Can you spot one that is not and why it is not? A/Because Black Mark

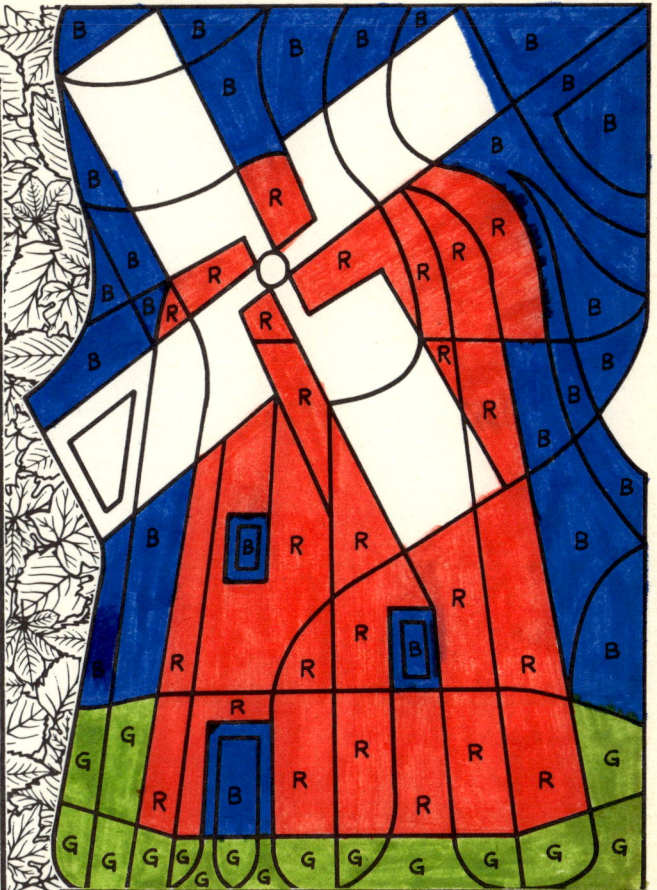

4 To discover what this object is colour the parts marked 'B' in blue 'G' in green and 'R' in brightest red. Have you ever seen one of these – if so, where?

5 Brock the badger never takes a wrong turn on his way home. Can you find the track he follows? Do you know what a badger's home is called?

DUSTY BIN SAYS...

FIND THE PAIRS!

EACH OBJECT MATCHES UP WITH ANOTHER OBJECT.

A
B
c
D
E
F
G
H
I
J
K
L

NOW SEE IF YOU CAN SAY WHICH NAME ON THE LEFT GOES WITH A NAME ON THE RIGHT TO MAKE A FAMOUS PAIR.

Darby	Gretel
Romeo	Ronnie
Hansel	Joan
Laurel	Wise
Morecambe	Juliet
Ronnie	Hardy

ANSWERS.

J - H
I - J
D - G
C - K
B - J
A - E

DARBY and JOAN,
ROMEO and JULIET,
HANSEL and GRETEL,
LAUREL and HARDY,
MORECAMBE and
WISE,
TWO RONNIES

It's on the house

1 The house above is a very nice one. Now draw in all the details on front of the outlined house below. Then why not colour both of them?

2 What is the object in the centre? All the things round are connected with it. Write the names of the things in the boxes beneath them.

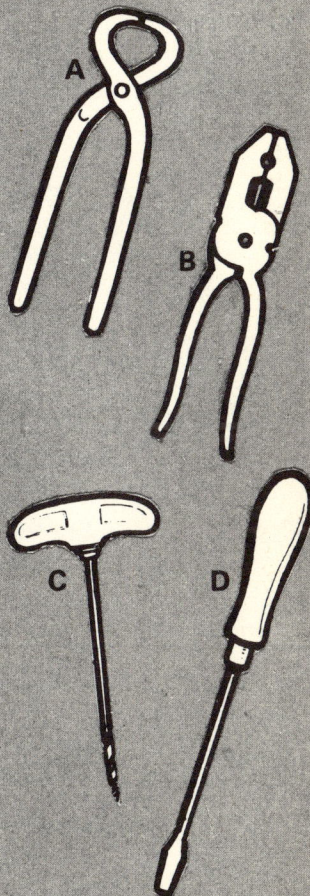

Answers:

People and pastimes

1 Here are three people with very different jobs. Write what they are in the boxes beneath the pictures. Some of the letters are there already to help you.

B				
D	N	E		

T		
C	I	R

B			
D	I	E	

2 The objects in the decoration below are clues to three popular party games played by young children. What games are they?

3 These are some groups of objects used by people who do certain jobs. Can you name the people? We have given you the first letter to help you.

G

A

C

Answers:
(1) Ballet dancer, Town crier, Bus driver. (2) Musical chairs, Oranges and lemons, 'Ring a ring o'roses.' (3) Gardener, artist, cook.

Hide and seek

1 Jenny and Adam were playing hide and seek in the woods when they realised that their dog, Jock, was missing. He had disappeared into the woods to look for the other creatures hidden there. Find Jock and as many others as you can. There are five others. What are they?

WHAT BIRDS ARE HIDING HERE?

RALK
NUTINGB INTRAM
LOWLAWS
RAWLEBR ROVELP
HURTHS CRUELW
HINTGINELGA
PIGEAM RINGLAST

2 The names of eleven wild birds are hidden in these scrambled words. Can you sort them out?

3 Shade in the shapes marked with a dot and you will discover an unusual little creature that you may find in a pool or stream.

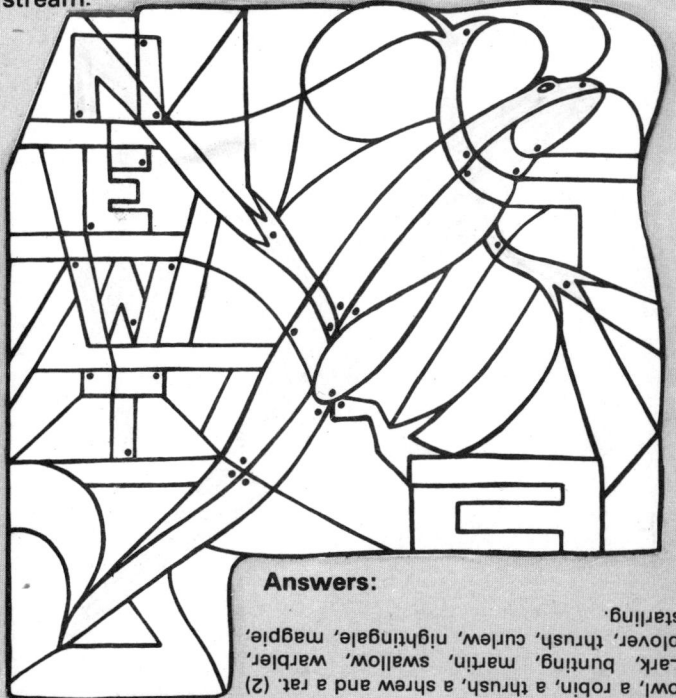

Answers:

(1) Hidden in the picture are: The dog, Jock, an owl, a robin, a thrush, a shrew and a rat. (2) Lark, bunting, martin, swallow, warbler, plover, thrush, curlew, nightingale, magpie, starling.

A page of mini word puzzles

1 A crossword with picture clues for you to solve.

to HJNO

to RYAM

to EPERT

PROVERB PUZZLER

2 A proverb is hidden in each of the panels below. Can you unravel the clues and find the proverbs?

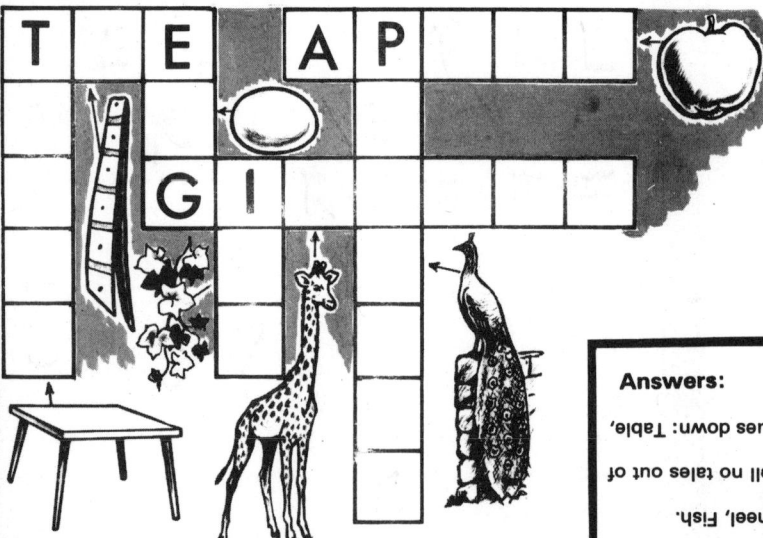

to TOYB

to NJEYN

4 Each label has the letters of someone's name written on it. Write the name in correctly in the space underneath the jumbled letters.

3 Another very mini crossword with picture clues.

28

Name these seabirds

and explore the depths of an exciting rock pool.

1 _____

2 _____

3 _____

4 _____

5 _____

6 What is hidden in this rock pool? Rock pools are always full of interesting things if you know what to look for. To find out what is here shade in all the parts marked with a dot.

7 Binoculars are useful at the seaside, but some binoculars are better than others. These four look the same, but one of them is not as good as the rest. Which one has something missing?

Answers:
(1) Blackheaded gull. (2) Blackbacked gull. (3) Puffin. (4) Gannet. (5) Cormorant. (6) In the pool is a jellyfish, seahorse, a fish, starfish, seaweed. (7) C. The ridges on the focusing barrel are missing.

DUSTY'S STAIRCASE PUZZLE

Each of the clues to this unusual crossword puzzle is a miniature Join-the-Dots. Solve each clue by joining the numbered dots together with straight lines and write your answers in the squares provided.

TRY IT ~ IT'S FUN!

Street scene

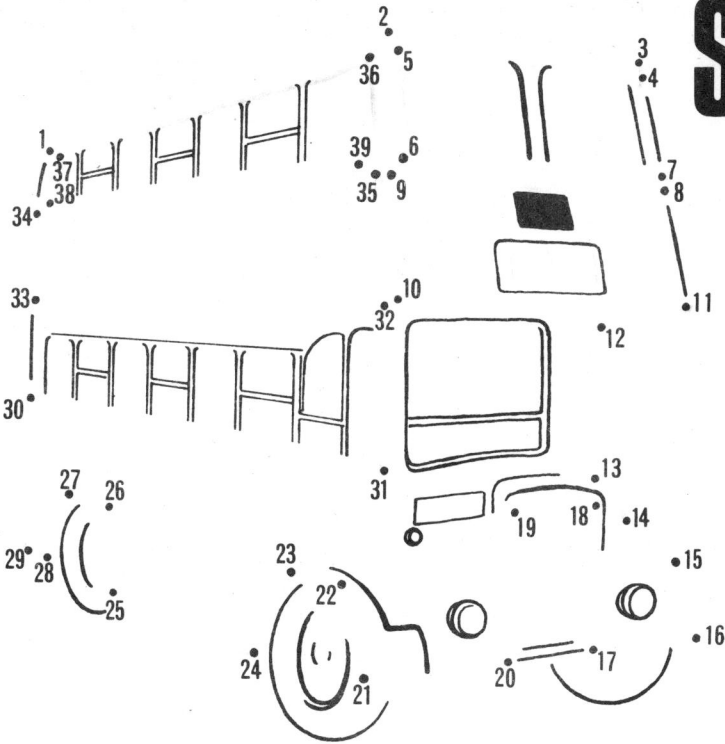

1 Join the dots from 1 to 39 to complete this picture of a double-decker bus. Then you can colour your drawing so that it looks like those you see in the streets.

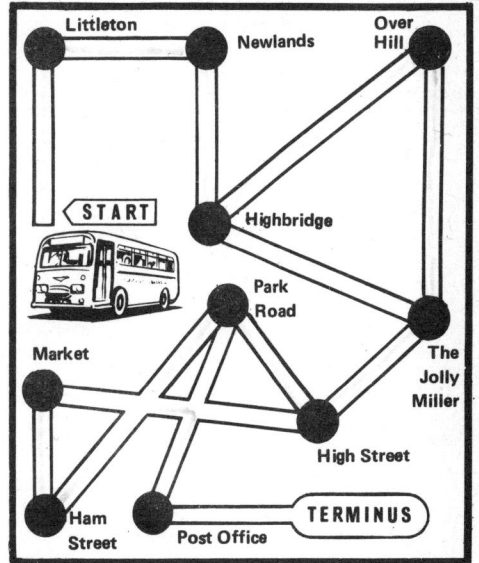

2 The coach driver has to call only once at each stop. He must not go along any road more than once, or cut across a road he has been along. What is his route?

3 There are many lanes through the wood but only one of them will take the twins to their caravan. Can you see their road?

Answers:

4 Our artist drew this rather nice street scene. Only when we looked more closely we found six mistakes. What are they?

Ones and twos...

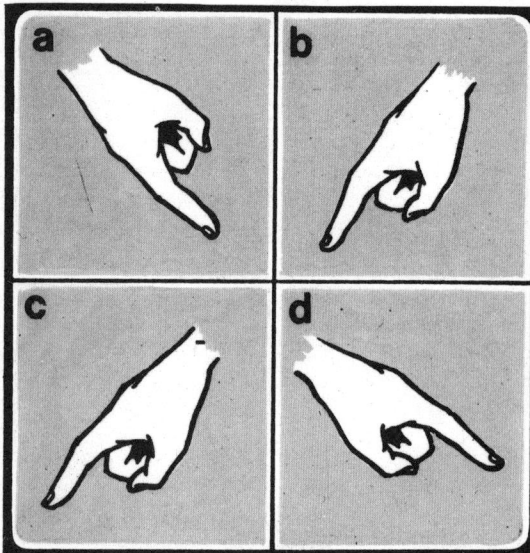

Find the odd ONE out

1 Four fingers pointing across the squares all look the same. Nevertheless one of them is different. Can you spot which one it is and say why?

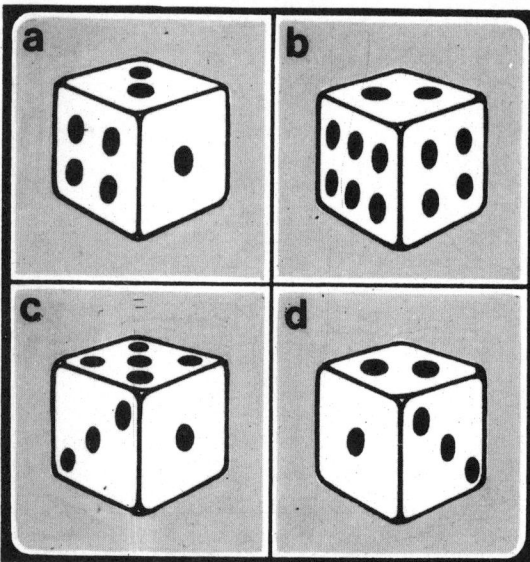

2 In contrast, here are four dice which all look different. But there is a connecting link between three of them, so once again there is an odd one that is different. What is the thing that makes three of them similar, and which is the odd one out?

TWO objects with ONE word to describe both . . .

3 The top and bottom pictures on the left show quite different objects which share the same name. Write in that name in the space.

TWO pictures to make ONE word.

4 The objects below are all different, but if you write down the name under each picture, each pair forms the name of another well-known object . . .

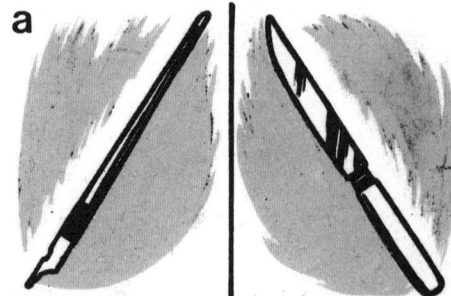

a

b

c

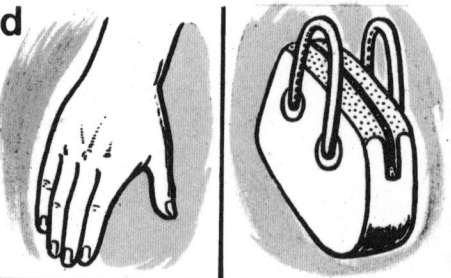

d

RHYMING PAIRS

Say the names of the objects on this page out loud, then pair up the ones that rhyme. Here is one pair for you: Ring and Spring. Now rhyme the other ten objects into five pairs.

ANSWERS:

33

THE SPOOKS OF ST. LUKE'S

41

After puzzling your brains over all the quiz questions and puzzles we have set you, we thought you'd like to relax for awhile in the company of Captain Codsmouth and Sir Munchkin — to say nothing of that priceless puss, Mowser.

CAP'N CODSMOUTH

CAP'N

BOSUN MULLIGAN

FRED NEEDLE

STOKER SPLITPIN

THE END

48

JOIN ALL THE NUMBERED DOTS TOGETHER WITH STRAIGHT LINES, FROM 1 TO 178, AND YOU WILL FIND YOU ARE DRAWING A SUPER PICTURE OF A — WELL, JOIN THE DOTS AND SEE!

WHEN YOU HAVE DONE THAT, COMPLETE THE PICTURE BY FOLLOWING THE ADDITIONAL INSTRUCTIONS BELOW ° ° ° °

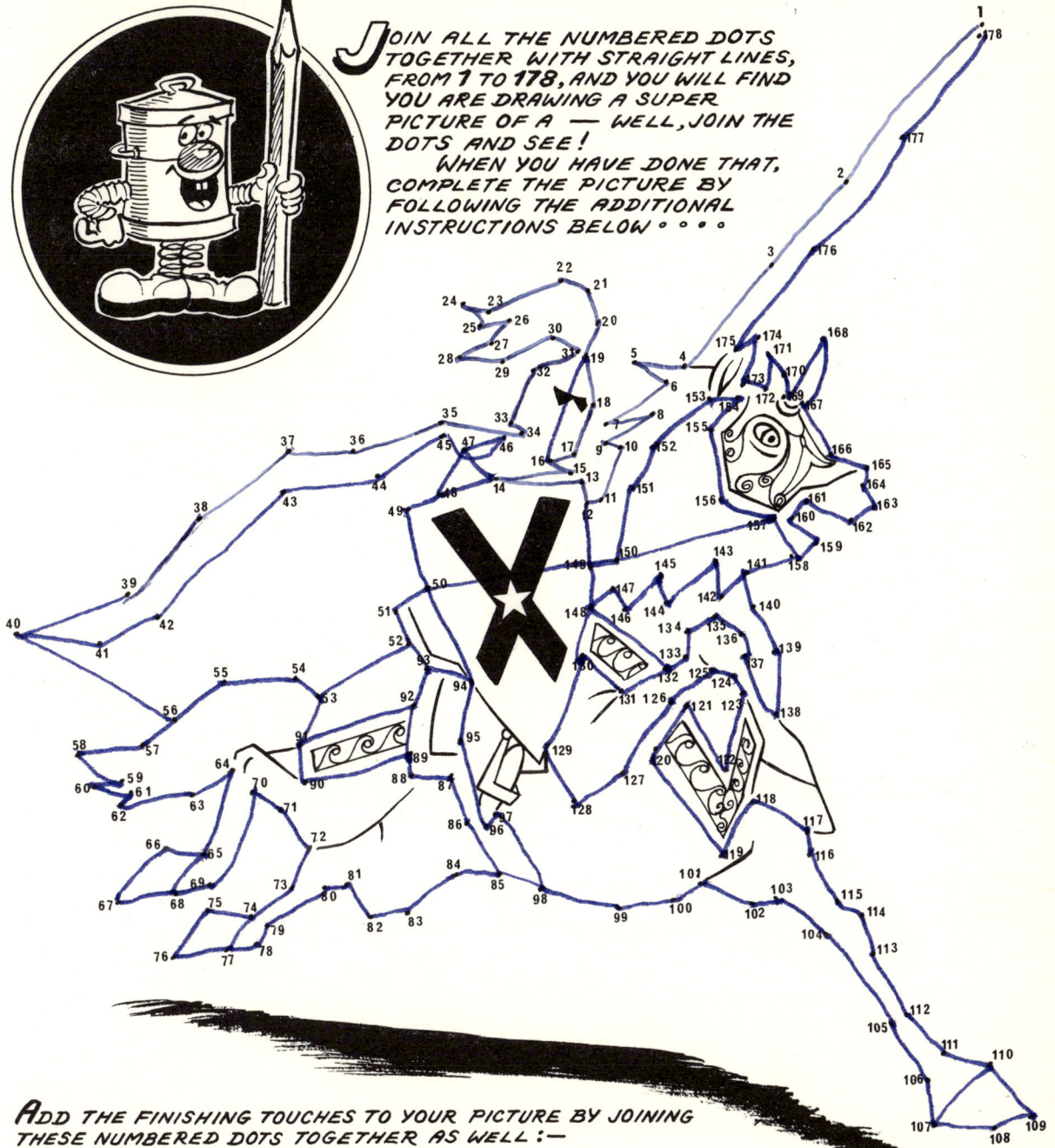

ADD THE FINISHING TOUCHES TO YOUR PICTURE BY JOINING THESE NUMBERED DOTS TOGETHER AS WELL :—

12 – 149	40 – 56	52 – 93	89 – 92	
14 – 47	50 – 94	65 – 68	107 – 110	141 – 158
14 – 48	50 – 157	74 – 77	130 – 148	
16 – 19	53 – 91	85 – 98	132 – 148	

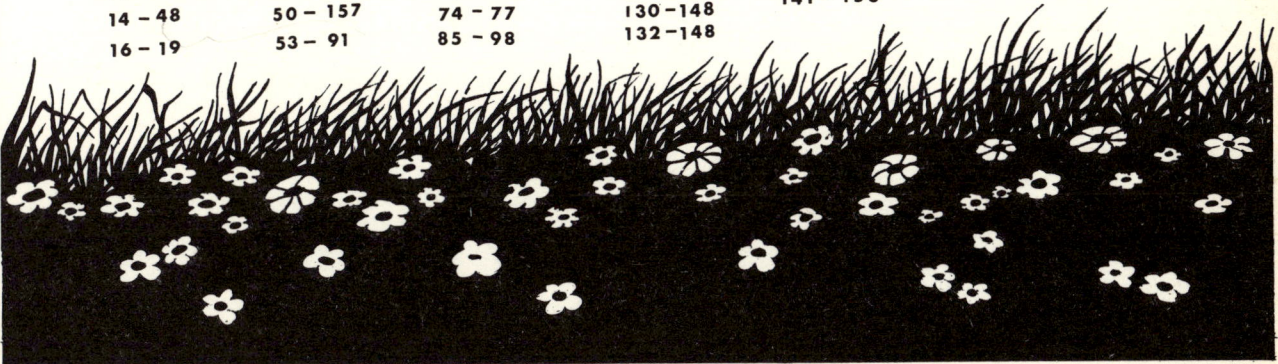

Observation and counting game

A game to test your quickness of eye and help your counting.

What is it?
Purple, yellow, red and green,
The king cannot reach it, nor even the queen,
Nor can the wizard,
    whose power is so great:
Now solve this riddle
    while I count to eight.

Answer to the riddle
A rainbow

A How many pageboys can you see in the picture ....

B How many of those pageboys have hats on? ......

C How many pageboys does that make without hats on? ....

D How many pageboys can you count with trumpets ....

E Now count all the pageboys without trumpets ....

F How many men and boys are wearing crowns? ....

G Now count all the women wearing crowns ....

H How many people wearing crowns does that make? ......

I How many dogs can you see in the picture? ....

J Now count all the dogs that are wearing crowns ......

K Count all the people that are wearing black stockings ....

L How many people are wearing white stockings? ....

M Now count all the spires on the castle ....

Answers: A.7, B.3, C.4, D.4, E.3, F.2, G.1, H.3, I.2, J.1, K.5, L.5, M.5.

50

DUSTY BIN DOWN THE MINE

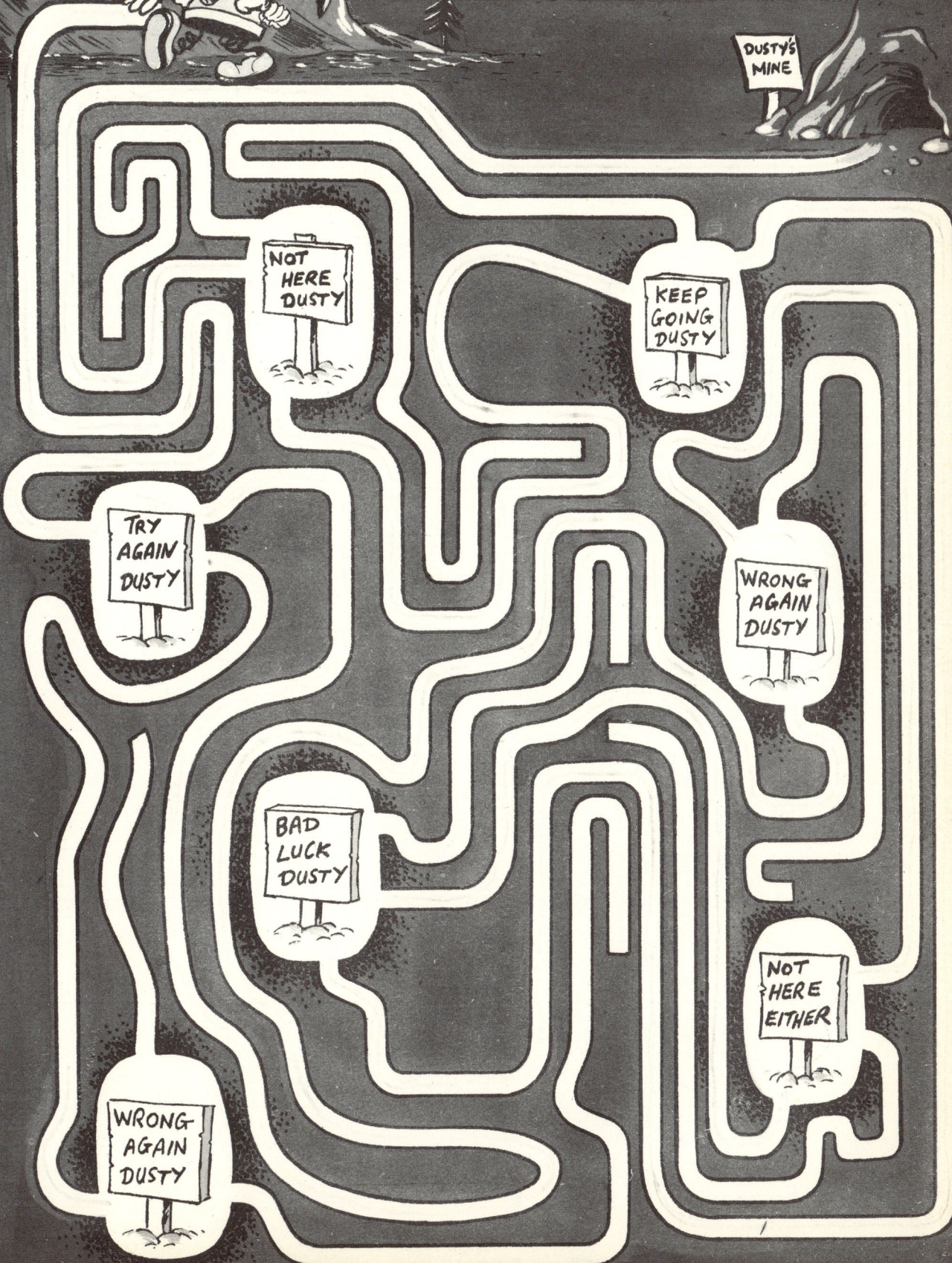

DUSTY'S MINE

NOT HERE DUSTY

KEEP GOING DUSTY

TRY AGAIN DUSTY

WRONG AGAIN DUSTY

BAD LUCK DUSTY

NOT HERE EITHER

WRONG AGAIN DUSTY

SPOT THE SAYINGS

1 — It's all your fault!

Tools never blames good his a workman.

2 — Glass-stones should not throw in people houses.

3 — Light work many hands' make.

4 — Two bush hand in the worth is a in the bird.

5 — Speed less more haste.

THE SAYINGS ARE **VERY** MIXED UP — BUT THE PICTURES SHOULD HELP YOU TELL WHAT THEY ARE. TRY HAVING A SAYING RACE WITH A PAL!

Answers

1- A GOOD WORKMAN NEVER BLAMES HIS TOOLS. 2- PEOPLE IN GLASS-HOUSES SHOULD NOT THROW STONES. 3- MANY HANDS MAKE LIGHT WORK. 4- A BIRD IN THE HAND IS WORTH TWO IN THE BUSH. 5- MORE HASTE LESS SPEED.

A CASE FOR INVESTIGATION!

Help Dusty Bin to solve this mysterious case! Fill in the missing letters on each of the eight labels and find out where this much travelled luggage has been.

GRAND HOTEL ★

Hôtel Splendide

1. — ON — ON

2. — IV — — PO — L

3. D — RB — N

4. NE — OR —

5. SA — — RA — CI — CO

6. B — MBA —

7. — ER — IN

8. — AR — S

53

Your Saturday Night

Ted

Compère -

Rogers

Ted Rogers, your stand-up comedian and master of the topical gag, has tasted life at all levels.

He was raised in the Kennington district of South London and went to the same school there that Charlie Chaplin attended. And today he plays polo, his favourite sport, with the elite at exclusive Cowdray Park, Sussex.

Ted, a civil servant's elder son, started in show business by doing an impersonation of Danny Kaye at a holiday camp talent contest when he was 14. He won — and then went on to impersonate other show business stars of the day, like Johnny Ray and Frankie Laine.

Before he was called up to do National Service in the RAF, Ted was offered £17.50 a week on a 32-week touring show called "Hollywood Doubles". It was big money for a young man — but he turned it down because he thought he would miss his Sunday soccer matches with his pals.

In the RAF, Ted began to take show business seriously. "I realised I could make a living out of making people laugh," he says.

"When I was demobbed I went to the Labour Exchange and told them I wanted to go into show business. They got me a job with a theatre ticket agency — £7 a week and luncheon vouchers. I had to give ticket numbers and prices so quickly that fast talking became a habit."

But he got himself an agent and understudied Tommy Steel as Buttons in "Cinderella". Tommy fell ill — and Ted took over and stole the show.

After becoming compère of a Shirley Bassey show at the Palladium, Ted took over as front man in *Sunday Night at the Palladium* in 1974. Stand-up comic jobs like these developed his flair and made him a natural for the smash-hit "3-2-1" show.

Ted sometimes records "3-2-1" four months ahead of screening. It takes three days to prepare and make one show. And he constantly worries about getting it right. "You can't take anything for granted in this business," he says.

His interest in polo developed when he met some players from Cowdray Park who were competing in Miami, where he was appearing in a show. Back home, he went to Cowdray Park to watch and was hooked. He learned to ride and now he has his own stable of polo ponies.

Ted met his second wife Marion, a former dancer, when he was in a Blackpool summer show. They live in a large detached bungalow with half an acre of land in Little Chalfont, Bucks.

He likes to get home as often as possible although he drives 70,000 miles a year to cabaret dates in his Mercedes, Ford Mustang, Vauxhall Royale or Datsun. He says: "The Mustang is my favourite. It passes everything on the motorway — except the petrol stations. That's its only trouble."

His proudest moment came when he appeared with Bing Crosby at New York's Avery Fisher Hall. He cracked a series of one-liner Nixon jokes — not knowing that the former President's daughter Tricia was in the audience. They brought the house down.

DOTTY FUN

There's something fishy afoot! Join up
the dots to find out what is going on.

DUSTY BIN'S Guide to Good Manners

Know your words

Here is a quiz that will help you to understand more words. One of the four examples with each word is the nearest in meaning to the word.

1. A *litigant* is (a) a lazy fellow; (b) someone who is spiteful; (c) an inflammable substance; (d) someone engaged in a lawsuit.
2. *Falsetto* means (a) in error; (b) high-pitched; (c) soft and slow; (d) hesitant.
3. *Hirsute* means (a) having a large beak; (b) hairy; (c) mentally retarded; (d) comical.
4. A *nomad* is (a) a wanderer; (b) a knowledgeable person; (c) a person whose duty it is not to fight; (d) an assumed name.
5. *Serried* means (a) having a notched edge; (b) well-served; (c) packed together; (d) in a serious manner.
6. *Ignominious* means (a) unknown; (b) disgraceful; (c) ignorant; (d) inflammable.
7. A *plumbline* is (a) a line of fruit trees; (b) an illness; (c) a crooked line; (d) a perpendicular line.
8. *Fickle* means (a) sharp; (b) generous; (c) changeable; (d) haughty.
9. *Illicit* means (a) incurably ill; (b) low-bred; (c) prohibited; (d) mean.
10. A *libation* is (a) an offering; (b) a speech; (c) a free pardon; (d) a harmful statement.
11. To *pulverize* is (a) to get ready for action; (b) to crush; (c) to punish; (d) to knock over.
12. *Nonchalant* means (a) stupid; (b) alien; (c) a non-combatant soldier; (d) indifferent.
13. An *epaulette* (or *epaulet*) is (a) shoulder ornamentation; (b) a duelling sword; (c) the end division of the brain; (d) a small fossil.
14. *Concave* is (a) a series of caves; (b) curving inwards; (c) curving outwards; (d) a meeting of cardinals.
15. *Palaver* means (a) like a palace; (b) pleasing to taste; (c) idle talk; (d) purple-coloured.
16. A *marauder* is (a) an ill-tempered person; (b) a type of rodent; (c) one who makes plundering raids; (d) an ancient mariner.
17. A *maelstrom* is (a) a Norwegian island; (b) a demon; (c) a whirlpool; (d) a small storm.
18. A *red-herring* is (a) Russian fish; (b) a bright idea; (c) a false trail; (d) a male salmon.
19. A *tarn* is (a) a lake; (b) a bird; (c) an insect; (d) a stream.
20. To *dilate* is (a) to go slowly; (b) to go carefully; (c) to grow smaller; (d) to grow larger.
21. *Poplin* is (a) an Alpine flower; (b) cotton fabric; (c) a favourite child; (d) part of a boat.
22. To *desiccate* is (a) to chop up; (b) to disapprove; (c) to dry; (d) to lose leaves.

This picture of Vikings can give you a clue to the answer to Question 16 – but there could be a catch in it!

By using your knowledge of familiar proverbs, can you answer these questions:

(a) What gathers no moss?
(b) Who spoiled the broth?
(c) Which waters run deep?
(d) What shouldn't be cried over?

QUICK QUIZ

Answers:
(a) A rolling stone,
(b) Too many cooks,
(c) Still waters,
(d) Spilt milk.

58

Answers

1. (d) Someone engaged in a lawsuit.

2. (b) A high male voice resembling the female voice in pitch; a forced shrill voice above the natural pitch.

3. (b) Hairy.

4. (a) A person who leads a wandering life, generally as an inhabitant of a country in a backward state of development.

5. (c) Packed compactly together, especially used by troops in close formation.

6. (b) Contemptible, base, dishonourable, disgraceful, inglorious.

7. (d) A device used by a mason for testing perpendiculars, consisting of a cord with a plumb (a weight) attached to it. A perpendicular line.

8. (c) Changeable, vacillating, inconstant.

9. (c) Prohibited, illegal.

10. (a) A liquid offering to the gods - normally of wine.

11. (b) To reduce to fine powder or dust. Also to destroy, crush, overwhelm.

12. (d) Exhibiting no response; indifferent, careless, cool.

13. (a) A piece of ornamentation on the shoulder of a uniform.

14. (b) Hollow, curving inwards, forming a curved hollow.

15. (c) A conference, or idle talk.

16. (c) ''Maraud'' is to plunder, pilfer or make raids for this purpose.

17. (c) A whirlpool.

18. (c) A point, topic or thing introduced to divert attention from the real matter at issue and set people on a false trail.

19. (a) A small lake on a mountainside or moor.

20. (d) To become larger, to expand, to grow wider and bigger.

21. (b) Fabric, originally of silk and worsted, now of cotton.

22. (c) To dry - especially to dry foods for preservation.

In the air

1 Join up the dots, starting at number one, to complete this picture. Can you describe what sort of machine it is?

2 Here are three unusual objects which you might see in the sky. Write what they are called in the panels beneath them. Which of them flies the highest?

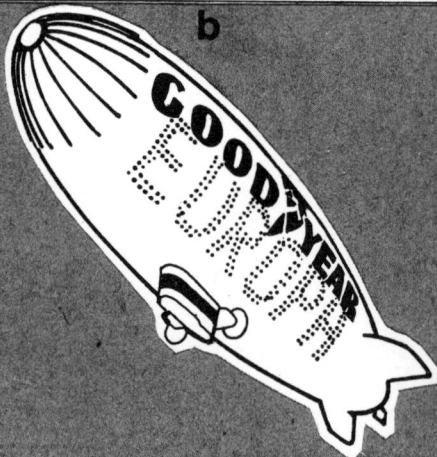

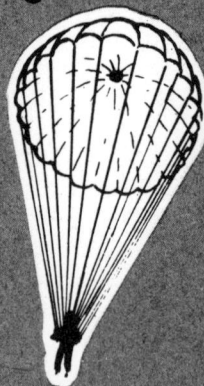

a

b

c

Cheeky Chappy

Join the dots 1-67 and you will see a fellow who brought a lot of fun to people in the past. Do you know what he is? When you have filled in his outline you can colour him using bright colours.

Answer:
A jester.

ON TARGET!

Make a ring of thin paper over the neck of a bottle. Place a coin on top of the paper ring, and handing your friends a pencil, challenge them to get the coin into the bottle using only the pencil.

When they give up, sharply tap the inside of the paper circle with your pencil and watch the coin drop into the bottle.

DUSTY BIN up to all sorts of tricks!

WALKING STICKS!

Slit the end of a match and sharpen the end of another so that it will pass through the slit to join both the matches together as shown.

Now rest the joined matches on the blade of a table knife and hold the knife so that the tips just touch the table-top. The matches will walk along the knife-blade!

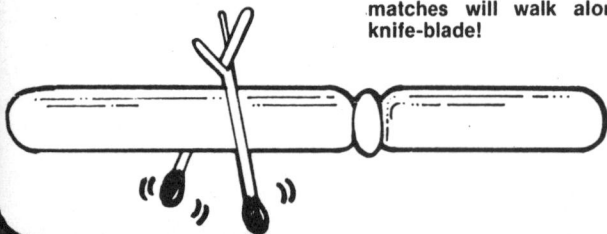

PAPER CATCH

Give a friend a fairly heavy book and a six-inch square of paper.

Now ask him to make a 'bridge' out of the paper to support the book.

When he's tried umpteen times until he's beaten, show him how.

All you do is cut the paper in half and fold each piece into pleats as the drawing shows.

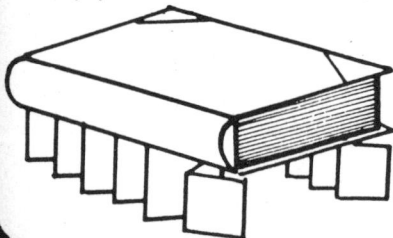

PENNY TEASER

Ask anyone if they can hold two pennies on top of each other using their index finger and thumb. Impossible? Not if you cut a matchstick so that it fits exactly the width of two pennies and place it behind the coins as the picture shows you, with the match facing you.

VANISHING PENNY

Here is a simple trick that will amaze your friends.

Take the tray from an empty match-box and cut an   inch slit in the bottom of one end, as the drawing shows. You'll have to use sharp knife to do this cleanly. So BE CAREFUL! Put the tray back in the cover and pop a few matches in the box this will make it look like a genuine, untouched box.

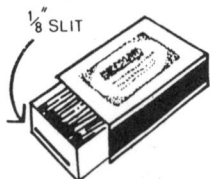

Now, when you are ready to perform the trick, you must hold the box with the slit towards you. Shake out the matches and pop the penny in.

Rattle the box for everyone to hear then let the coin drop through the slit into your hand. Now open the match-box show everyone that it is empty!

Ask your friends if they can balance a matchstick on its head without striking the match or using anything sticky.

It won't be long before they give up, for you to show them how . . .

Wrap a tiny piece of silver paper from a cigarette pack or bar of chocolate round the match-head and put it headfirst into a glass of water. The matchstick will float, balanced upright, as the drawing shows.

1/8" SLIT

MAKE A MICROSCOPE

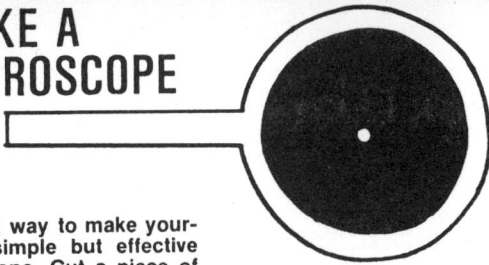

Here's a way to make yourself a simple but effective microscope. Cut a piece of cardboard to the shape shown and draw a circle about the size of a penny on the large round end. Paint this circle black with indian ink, and then make a pin-hole in the centre of it. Hold this up to one eye, close the other eye and peep through the hole. Everything seems magnified.

VANISHING COLOURS

Cut a disc about three inches round out of a postcard, and paint or crayon in YELLOW, RED and BLUE.

Stick a pencil through the centre as shown.

Rub the pencil hard in the palms of your hands. The disc spins round and the colours will entirely disappear!

PENCIL PRANKS

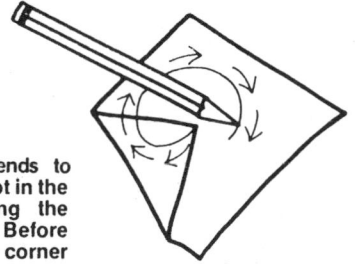

Ask any of your friends to draw a circle with a dot in the centre without taking the pencil from the paper. Before you start, fold over a corner of the paper and make your dot. Now, without taking your pencil off the paper, begin drawing your circle over the fold, continuing the line on to the rest of the paper when you release it.

INSTANT KNOT

Ask your friends to tie a knot in a length of cord using only ONE HAND. It's dead easy when you know how . . . Take a piece of cord about four feet in length and hold it as shown in the first diagram. End X should hang down about a foot. All you have to do is to turn your hand over in the direction shown by the arrow and grasp end X between your thumb and forefinger. Then shake your hand, so that the loop around your hand falls off and there is a knot! When you have learned to do it quickly, it will look to your audience as if you simply gave the rope a shake and made a knot.

HOW MANY SQUARES?

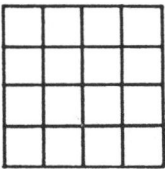

How many squares in this diagram . . .? If you say 16 look again: there are 30.

MAGIC SQUARE

However you add a row of figures in this square, they'll make 34. Divide it into four smaller squares. The figures will again add up to 34. And the centre square adds up to the same!

16	3	2	13
5	10	11	8
9	6	7	12
4	15	14	1

PAPER MAGIC

Borrow a small coin and place it in the centre of a square piece of paper. Fold the paper up and give it to your pal then watch his face when he unfolds it to find the money's GONE!

The secret's in the way you fold the paper as in the sketch. Lay it down and start by folding over the inside lines, begining with the sides. Pick it up to make the final folds; the coin secretly slides out into your hand.

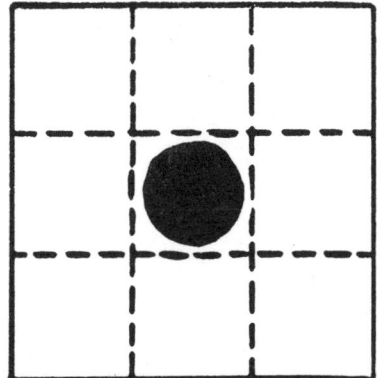

Memory Game

Below this funny picture are some questions to test your memory. First cover these questions and study the picture carefully for one minute. Then cover the picture and see how many questions you can answer correctly. Write your answers on a piece of paper then see if you were right.

In a field, behind some tents
I saw an elephant jump a fence
He jumped so high he touched the sky
And didn't come back till the Fourth of July.

THE WORLD'S HIGHEST JUMPING ELEPHANT

1 What event is about to take place in the picture?

2 Where is it all happening?

3 Does it look as if it is a windy day?

4 How many people have umbrellas?

5 What is the elephant wearing?

6 What are the keepers doing?

7 What does it say on the notice board?

8 How many birds are sitting on the notice board?

9 How high did the elephant jump?

10 When did he return?

Answers:
(1) An elephant is going to jump over a fence.
(2) In a field behind some tents.
(3) Yes, the flags are blowing about.
(4) One woman.
(5) A little hat or skullcap and a blanket or cloth.
(6) They are pushing the elephant to make him jump.
(7) The world's highest jumping elephant.
(8) Four.
(9) He touched the sky.
(10) The fourth of July.

64

Know Your Colours

HERE ARE SOME WELL-KNOWN OBJECTS THAT I'M SURE YOU'LL RECOGNISE. BUT CAN YOU PAINT IN THE CORRECT COLOURS, GIRLS AND BOYS? YOU WILL COLLECT A POINT FOR EACH ONE YOU COLOUR CORRECTLY!

1

2

3

4

5

6

7

ANSWERS:—

1. Red, white and blue. 2. Red, amber and green. 3. Green. 4. Amber. 5. Red. 6. Red. 7. Red and black.

Meet the man who

A dustbin is not the most likeliest of TV stars. But Dusty Bin who appears in Yorkshire Television's quiz show, "3-2-1", hosted by the inimitable Ted Rogers is just that. However, this particular dustbin has managed to take on a life of its own, thanks to the mechanical ingenuity of Ian Rowley, an electronic genius. Rowley has a small workshop near Leeds, where he makes props and special effects with his father for TV and film companies.

Dusty has come a long way since he was first trundled on to the screen. Four years ago, he went electronic, when Ian stuffed him with microprocessors, silicon chips and an assortment of motors, at a development cost of some £10,000. As a result, Dusty's popularity grew and grew, until he eventually became a star in his own right who receives regular fan mail.

Since he has become an electronic wizard, Ian's life has almost revolved around Dusty Bin, who performs a different trick for each show. In addition, he has to be provided with a change of costume each week. "To begin with there were other problems," Ian says. "As Dusty spent the first two years of his life on castors, he wasn't originally built as a radio controlled robot. This gave rise to a number of headaches. For one thing, radio control was especially difficult in a studio, where there is massive interference from all the equipment. Most of these problems have now been solved, but I have to be there for the rehearsals and the actual performance just in case something goes wrong. And, of course, I have to control him."

Here is another of the many costumes Dusty Bin has worn on 3-2-1.

made DUSTY BIN □ □ □

Ian's family background is not the most obvious one for someone in his line of business. His grandfather and great grandfather were Music Hall performers. His great grandfather, a comedian, was in the very first Royal Variety Performance in 1912. His own father, Alf Rowley, was trained as a scenic artist in Leeds. It was Alf who started the family business in 1948. Ian joined him when he left school. There are just the two of them, so it is very much a family business.

Some of their earliest television work was for Harry Corbett and Sooty, for whom they made innumerable props and tricks. They built all the amazing gadgets that Magnus Pike waved his arms over in the long running, "Don't Ask Me." For a drama series, "The Brontës of Howarth," they reproduced many of the original pieces of furniture from the Howarth parsonage. They made all of Les Dawson's personal props from collapsing pianos to underwater bagpipes. For the drama series, "Airline," they built a life-size mock-up cockpit interior of a DC3, with exact copies of its instrumentation, complete with movement simulation. Nothing, it would seem, is too large or small for the Rowleys to tackle.

Recently, an electronic scorpion was required for the TV serial, "The Jewel in the Crown". It was something that needed a great deal of electronic know-how to make it move convincingly. The fact that Ian managed to solve it, as he does all the other problems given him, is possibly rather remarkable, when one learns that he taught himself electronics by studying at home.

Ted Rogers, the star of 3-2-1, takes a little time off to have his picture taken with Dusty Bin and his creator, Ian Rowley.

RESCUE DUSTY!

MOWSER and his Enemy JAMES
THE PRICELESS PUSS   the Butler

PHEW! IT'S *TOO HOT* SITTING IN THE SUN!

I DON'T MIND SITTING IN THE SUNSHINE!

MOVE MY CHAIR INTO A *SHADY SPOT*, JAMES!

I'LL COLLAPSE THE DECK-CHAIR TO CARRY IT! ER — SORRY, MOWSER! I DON'T THINK! HA! HA!

WHOP

I'D LIKE ONE OF *THESE!* THEN I'D KEEP *COOL* IN THE SUNNY WEATHER!

I'LL *MAKE YOU ONE,* YOUR LORDSHIP! I'M RATHER *HOT STUFF* AS A *CARPENTER!*

GARDEN NEWS
A NEW SWIVEL GARDEN HUT FOR MAXIMUM SHADE
FITTED ON A TURNTABLE TO ALLOW THE OCCUPANT TO KEEP TURNING AWAY FROM THE SUN...

AND LATER...

THERE, YOUR LORDSHIP! SIT INSIDE IN THE *SHADE!* YOU CAN *TURN AWAY FROM* THE SUN WHEN YOU FEEL *TOO HOT!*

GOODOH!

TOOLS

WHILE HIS LORDSHIP SETTLED HIMSELF *INSIDE,* SOME BIRDS SETTLED *ON TOP* . . .

NOW YOU'LL KEEP COOL, SIR!

I'LL CHASE OFF THOSE SAUCY BIRDS!

SCRAM!

WHIZZ

WHIZZ

CRASH

HOTHOUSE TROPICAL PLANTS

WHY DON'T YOU SIT STILL IN THE *SHADE*, SIR? — IT'S *RATHER HOT* OUT HERE!

AND IT'S GOING TO GET *HOTTER — FOR YOU!* YOU *STUPID* BUTLER!

OLD JAMES IS GETTING QUITE A *TAN* — RUNNING AROUND IN THE SUNSHINE!

129	130	131	132	133	134	135	136
128	127	126	125	124	123	122	121
97	98	99	100	101	102	103	10
96	95	94	93	92	91	90	89
65	66	67	68	69	70	71	72
64	63	62	61	60	59	58	57
33	34	35	36	37	38	39	40
32	31	30	29	28	27	26	25
1	2	3	4	5	6	7	8

''Here is a game for you to play with your family and friends,'' says Dusty Bin. To play it you will need different coloured counters and a dice. If you haven't got these things you can make a dice out of a matchbox, writing the numbers 1 to 6 on the sides, and use buttons instead of

Dusty Bin goes Fishing

How many can you count?